BASIC READING SERIES

LEVEL C

Six Ducks in a Pond

by Donald Rasmussen and Lynn Goldberg

Columbus, Ohio

A Division of The McGraw-Hill Companies

SRA/McGraw-Hill

A Division of The **McGraw·Hill** *Companies*

Send all inquiries to:
SRA/McGraw-Hill
8787 Orion Place
Columbus, OH 43240-4027

Printed in the United States of America.

ISBN 0-02-684001-4

6 7 8 9 0 RRC 07 06

Contents

Section 1

word lists 2
Six Pet Cats 4
Bess 9
Up to the Top 11

Section 2

word lists 15
sentences 16
The Duck and the Hen 17
My Doll 20
The Red Tug 21

Section 3

word lists 25
sentences 26
Ann Lends a Hand 27
Ten Lads 31
The Bug 32

Section 4

word lists 36
sentences 37
Red Hen's Eggs 38
The Best Doll 42
Jill's Best Pet 43
Just Ask 47

Section 5

word lists 48

sentences 50

The Elf Is Back 51

Rex and the Raft 54

Section 6

word lists 58

sentences 60

A Bug on a Plum 61

To Be Big 63

The Plan 68

The Pond 73

Section 7

word lists 76

sentences 78

Six Ducks in a Pond 79

Stan's Test 85

The Top 89

Section 8

word lists 90

sentences 92

The Best Band 93

Skip Gets a Crab 94

Gram's Plan 101

Brad and the Frog 106

The Best Fox in the Land 110

Section 9

word lists 116

sentences 118

The Trick Clock 119

Jim's Dog, Sniff 125

The Grill 130

Camp Six-by-Six 132

The Elf Gets Help 136

Pattern pages 143

__ll

		bell	Bill	doll	dull
		fell	fill		gull
		Nell	hill		hull
		sell	Jill		
		tell	kill		
		well	mill		
		yell	pill		
			till		
			will		

__ss

lass	Bess	hiss		fuss
mass	less	kiss		muss
pass	mess	miss		Russ

__ff

		Jeff			cuff
					huff
					puff

__zz

			fizz		buzz
					fuzz

__dd

	add			odd	

__nn

	Ann		inn		

__gg

	egg			

Six Pet Cats

Miss Hull had six pet cats—Muff, Cuff,

Huff, Puff, Ruff, and E. Nuff.

Miss Hull had the cats in a pen.

Miss Hull fed the cats well.

The cats got big, but the pen did not.

So the cats did not fit in the pen.

"Jim Bell, at the Red Mill Inn, has a

big pen," said Miss Hull.

"I will sell the cats to him."

So Miss Hull began to yell, "Let's go,
Muff! Let's go, Cuff! Let's go, Huff,
Puff, and Ruff! Let's go, E. Nuff!"

The six cats began to hop up on Miss Hull.
"The Red Mill Inn is at the top of a hill,"
said Miss Hull. "I cannot get to it if my
cats hop up. I will get a big box."

Miss Hull got the six cats into a box.
The cats began to fuss. Miss Hull said,
"Sit in the box till I get to the inn."
But Muff and Cuff began to tug at the box.

"I cannot lug a box of bad cats up a
hill," said Miss Hull. "I will get a bus.
The cats will not fuss in a box on a bus."
So Miss Hull got on a bus and sat.
The box was on Miss Hull's lap.

Nell Wells got on the bus.

Nell had a dog, Rags.

The bus man said, "No dogs on my bus."

But Rags ran on the bus and up to Miss Hull.

The cats in the box began to fuss and hiss.

Miss Hull got up.

The box of cats fell!

Muff, Cuff, Huff, Puff, Ruff, and E. Nuff
began to yell.

Miss Hull and Nell Wells began to yell.

The bus man began to yell!

It was a mess!

The six cats ran zigzag on the bus.

"I cannot run the bus!" said the bus man.

"Rags and the cats CANNOT run in my bus,

and the bus has to go!"

So Rags sat.

And the cats sat.

Nell Wells said to the bus man,

"Run the bus to the top of the hill.

Go to the Red Mill Inn, and I will get

Rags up."

The bus man was mad.

But the bus man ran the bus up the hill.

Nell Wells ran into the Red Mill Inn,

got a pan of ham, and set it in the inn.

A lot of ham was in the pan.

Rags said, "Yip, yip!" and sat up to beg.

"Run, Rags!" Nell began to yell.

"Run into the inn and get the pan of ham!"

Rags ran into the inn to get the ham.

Muff, Cuff, Huff, Puff, Ruff, and E. Nuff

got into the box.

Miss Hull got the box to Jim Bell, and

the bus man ran his bus.

Bess

Bess was not well.

So Mom said Bess had to get into bed.

"Why is Bess in bed?" said Dad.

"Bess is ill," said Mom. "I will not
let Bess get up till Bess gets well."

So Bess had to miss a lot of fun.

And it was not fun to get pills.

"Bess is sad," said Dad. "I can tell.
I will get Bess a big box."

Dad sat on the sill.

A BIG box was on his lap.

"A box!" said Bess. "My, it's big!
Is a pup in it?"

"No," said Dad. "A pup is fun, but a
pup will mess up a bed."

"Well," said Bess, "is it a hat?
It is! I can tell it's a hat!"

"No," said Dad, "it's not a hat.
A big hat is no fun in bed."

Dad set the box on Bess's bed.
Bess began to tug at the top of the box.
Pop! the top was up! And in the box was—
"A doll! A BIG doll!" Bess had to yell.

The doll got a hug and a kiss.
And so did Dad.

Up to the Top

Hop! Hop! Hop!

  Hop! Hop! Hop!

Up the hill ran a hen

  To get to the top.

Hip! Hip! Hop!

  Hip! Hip! Hop!

On the hill, the hen fell.

  Will it get to the top?

Hop! Hop! Hop!

  Hop! Hop! Hop!

Up the hill ran a pig

  To get to the top.

Hip! Hip! Hop!

  Hip! Hip! Hop!

On the hen, the pig fell.

  Will it get to the top?

11

Hop! Hop! Hop!

Hop! Hop! Hop!

Up the hill ran a fox

To get to the top.

Hip! Hip! Hop!

Hip! Hip! Hop!

On the hen

And on the pig,

The fox fell.

Will it get to the top?

Hop! Hop! Hop!

Hop! Hop! Hop!

Up the hill ran a man

To get to the top.

Hip! Hip! Hop!

Hip! Hip! Hop!

On the hen

And on the pig

And on the fox,

The man fell.

Will the man get to the top?

Hop! Hop! Hop!

Hop! Hop! Hop!

The man had a fox.

The man had a pig.

And the man had a hen.

But did the man get to the top?

__ck				
back	deck	Dick	cock	duck
Jack	neck	kick	dock	luck
pack	peck	lick	lock	suck
sack		Nick	rock	tuck
tack		pick	sock	
		Rick		
		sick		
		tick		

be
he
me
we
she

"It's fun to be in the sun," said Nell.

"Yes, but can we run?" said Nick.

"No, we cannot," she said.

"Why not?" said Nick.

"It is hot in the sun," Nell said. So she sat on a log, and he dug a pit.

"Dig me a big pit," Nell said. So he did.

The Duck and the Hen

A hen and a duck sat by a rock on a hill.

It was wet on the hill.

So the hen and duck had to sit in the mud.

"I will get sick if I sit in the mud,"

said the hen.

"And I am sick of the mud," said the

duck. "So I will get up on the rock.

The rock is not big, but I can sit on it."

The duck ran to the rock.

So did the hen. The duck fit on the rock.

But the hen did not.

The hen fell into mud up to its neck.

The hen said, "I will peck and kick if
I cannot sit on the rock."

But the duck sat on the rock.

The hen said, "The duck is not my pal.
She is on the rock, and I am in the mud.
I will get wet and sick."

As the duck sat on the rock, she said,
"I am sad. I miss the hen.
I can sit on the rock, but I miss my pal."

So she said to the hen, "Get up.
We can fit on the rock."

"Can we?" said the hen.

"Yes," said the duck.

"We can fit if you get onto my back."

Hop! Hop! The hen got on the duck's back.

The duck sat on the rock, and the hen sat on the duck.

"My pal," said the duck.

"My pal," said the hen.

"We CAN fit on the rock," said the hen and the duck.

My Doll

My doll is big.

   My doll has fun.

My doll can kick.

   My doll can run.

My doll was sick.

   My doll was not well.

My doll had bad luck

   And fell, fell, fell.

I ran to my doll.

   I fed it a pill.

My doll got so well,

   It ran up a hill.

The Red Tug

Jack and Jill ran a red tug.

It was not big, but it did go on big jobs.

Jack said, "Let's go to the dock, Jill.
We will get a big job if we can get to the
dock by ten."

"O.K.," said Jill. "Let's go."

Jill began to run the tug. Puff! Puff!

It ran on and on.

But Jack and Jill had a bit of bad luck.
The tug ran into a fog.

"We will miss the dock in the fog,"
said Jack. "We will pass it by."

"No," said Jill, "we will not miss it."

"But we will run onto the rocks," said
Jack.

Jill said, "We will go by the map.
We will zigzag and miss the rocks.
And if we go up to the rocks, a bell will
tell us."

"Will we get to the dock by ten?" said
Jack.

"If the sun will get rid of the fog, we can be at the dock by ten," said Jill.

"I will go back on deck," said Jack. Jack got wet in the fog on the deck. His cap fell to the deck, and it got wet.

But Jack said, "Jill will get us to the dock. She can and she will." The tug ran on in the wet, wet fog.

But it began to get hot. The sun began to get rid of the fog.

Jack began to yell, "The sun! The sun! We will get to the dock yet! And we will get to it by ten!"

"Yes," said Jill, "we will."

She ran the tug up to the dock.

It was not yet ten.

So Jill and Jack got the big job.

And the red tug did it well.

"We did it," said Jack.

"Luck and the sun did it," said Jill.

__nd				
band	bend	wind	fond	
hand	lend		pond	
land	mend			
sand	send			
and	end			

__nt				
can't	bent	hint		hunt
pants	dent	mint		
ant	lent	tint		
	rent			
	sent			
	tent			
	went			

25

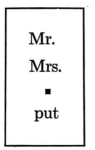

Mr.
Mrs.
■
put

Mr. Kent said to Mrs. Kent, "Is Bess set to go on the hunt?"

Mrs. Kent said to Bess, "Put on a hat, so we can go."

Bess said, "I DID put on my hat!"

Mrs. Kent said to Mr. Kent, "Bess has put on a hat. We can go."

Ann Lends a Hand

"Ann! Ann!" Nell began to yell.

"Jill! Jill! Jill! Lend me a hand.

I am on an egg hunt.

I will win the hunt if I can get

six eggs."

"I will lend a hand," said Ann.

"I will go to the top of the hill.

I can get six eggs to win the hunt."

"And I will lend a hand," said Jill.

"I will go to the pond.

The ducks and gulls at the pond will

lend us six eggs."

So Ann went up the hill.

And Jill went to the pond.

At the pond Jill met a duck and the
duck had six eggs in a sack.

"Sell me the sack of eggs, Mrs. Duck,"
said Jill.

"If I lend six eggs to Nell, she can win
an egg hunt."

"I cannot sell you my eggs," said the duck,

"but go to the gull by the dock.

She has eggs to sell."

So Jill went to the gull by the dock

and said, "Mrs. Gull, sell me six eggs.

My pal Nell has to get six eggs to win

an egg hunt."

But the gull said, "I cannot sell

an egg to Nell.

Mrs. Kent's dog was on a hunt and he got

MY eggs!"

Jill was sad as she went back to Nell.

She said to Nell,

"I had bad luck. Not an egg did I get.

I cannot lend a hand to win the egg hunt."

Ann ran back to Nell.

"Nell! Nell! I got the eggs! I got the eggs!"

Ann said, "Nell, I went to the top of the hill.

On the top of the hill was a rock.

And on the rock was an ant.

The ant had six eggs to sell.

So—I got the six eggs.

The eggs are not big—but six ant eggs

will win an egg hunt!

Did I lend a hand?"

Ten Lads

A band of ten lads

Had put up a tent

On the sand by a pond,

And in the lads went.

The lads had ten backpacks

And ten pans and pots.

And the lads had a rug

And a mop and ten cots.

But the wind put an end

To the tent on the sand.

And the ants in the beds

Put an end to the band.

The Bug

Rick Bond had a net.

A pal had sent it to him.

Rick went to his mom and said,

"Mom, can I go on a hunt?

I will get my pack.

I will put my net in it.

I will go to the back.

I bet I can get a bug."

"Get a bug?" said Mrs. Bond.

"Yes," said Rick.

"I will put a bit of ham on a log.

A bug is fond of ham.

I will get in back of a log.

The bug will run up to get the ham.

And BAP!—my net will get him.

Can I go, Mom?"

"No, Rick," said his mom.

"It's wet in back."

"But, Mom," said Rick,

"I am big, and I can hunt.

I will not get wet, and I WILL get a bug."

So, Mrs. Bond said, "O.K."

Rick put his pack on his back.

He put his net in his pack.

And he went to the back.

He put up his tent in back of a log.

He got in back of the log.

But he fell and cut his hand on a rock.

And he got rips in his pants and socks.

The net fell into the mud and got a rip.

It was a mess, and so was Rick.

Rick said, "I can't mend my pants!

I can't mend my socks!

I can't fix my net. Why—I can't hunt!

It's as bad as Mom said it was."

So he went into the tent and sat on his

pack. He was sad.

He said, "My luck is bad!

I will go back to Mom."

But as Rick said it, a big bug ran into his tent.

It ran up to Rick as he sat on his pack.

Rick did not yell.

He did not pick up his net.

He got up and ran. He ran back to his mom.

He got into his mom's lap.

 "Mom! Mom!" said Rick.

"A bug DID run up. But I did not get it.

It was a hunt—but the bug was on the

hunt, and I was on the run!"

__st

fast	best	fist		dust
last	nest	list		just
past	pest	mist		must
	rest			rust
	test			
	vest			
	west			

__sk

mask	desk			dusk
task				husk
ask				tusk

36

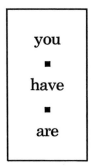

you

■

have

■

are

"Are the ducks in the pen?" said Nell.

"Yes," said Dad. "The ducks are in

the pen."

"Have you put the hens in the pen?"

said Nell.

"No, I have not," Dad said. "Have you?"

Red Hen's Egg

Mrs. Redfox had a hen pen.

The hens in the pen let Mrs. Redfox have eggs.

She sent the eggs to Miss West to sell.

Red Hen and six big hens sat on nests
in the pen. The six big hens had eggs.
But Red Hen did not. She was sad.

"I must have an egg," Red Hen said.
"I will sit on the nest till I have an egg."

She sat and sat. At last she had an egg.

It was a BIG, BIG egg.

Mrs. Redfox went to get the eggs.

"Hens," she said, "let's have the eggs.

I must put the eggs into a box.

And I must send it to Miss West to sell."

She went to the nests of the six hens.

She put a hand into the nests and got

the eggs. And she put the eggs into a box.

"Well, Red," she said to Red Hen,

"will you let me have an egg?"

"I have a BIG, BIG egg," Red Hen said,

"but you can't have it.

You can't put it into the box.

And you must not sell it."

"But Red," said Mrs. Redfox,

"I must have the egg to fill the box.

If I can't have it, Miss West will not sell

the rest."

But Red Hen just sat on the nest.

She just sat on the big egg.

She did not let Mrs. Redfox have it.

"Red Hen," said Mrs. Redfox, "you are the last hen I can ask. If I can't fill the box, I can't sell the rest of the eggs."

Red Hen got mad. She said, "If you put a hand into my nest, I will peck it! You can't have my egg, Mrs. Redfox!"

"But the egg you have will be the
best in the box," said Mrs. Redfox.

"My egg will be the BEST?" said Red Hen.

"Yes, yes!" said Mrs. Redfox.

"Will you TELL Miss West my egg is the
best egg?" said Red Hen.

"I will," said Mrs. Redfox.
"I will tell Miss West it is Red Hen's egg,
and it is the best egg in the land."

"O.K.," said Red Hen. "You can have it.
Just tell Miss West it is the best egg in the box,
and I will let you add it to the rest.
And I will sit on my nest. I will sit and sit.
I will get you lots of big eggs to sell."

And she did.

The Best Doll

If you must have a doll,

And you must have the best,

Well, you must pick ME!

I can pass the test.

I can tag, jog, and run

Just as fast as the rest.

I will have lots of fun,

But will not be a pest.

I will not fuss and yell

If you ask me to nap,

But will just go "ho-hum"

And will rest in a lap.

Jill's Best Pet

Jill was six, and she had pets.

She had a pet cat and a pet dog.

And she had a pet duck.

"My pet cat and dog are lots of fun,

but my best pet is Bess, my duck,"

Jill said.

If Jill ran, Bess ran.

If Jill had to rest, Bess had to rest.

If Jill got sick, Bess got sick.

If Jill had fun, Bess had fun.

But Bess was a bad duck.

If Bess met a man, she ran to peck him.

At 6 P.M. Mom said, "Jill, go get Dad.

But you must not let Bess go.

She will peck him."

So Jill said, "Bess, I must get Dad.

But you can't go.

Why not just run to the pond?

You will not be a pest at the pond."

But Bess did not go to the pond.

As Jill ran fast to get Dad, so did Bess.

Bess got to him just as Jill did.

And Bess ran past Jill to Dad.

She ran up to him to peck his leg.

Dad was mad. "Bess is bad," he said.

"She bit me, Jill.

You just can't have Bess as a pet."

Jill was upset. She said,

"Bess is not a bad pet. She is my pal.

If you pet Bess, she will not peck you.

You did not pet Bess, so she bit you."

"O.K.," said Dad, "I will pet Bess.

But if she pecks me, she must go!"

"Bess will not peck you," said Jill.

Dad sat and began to pet Bess.

And Bess did not peck him.

"Jill, I am not mad at Bess," he said.

"She is not bad.

You can have Bess as a pet."

Bess the duck was Jill's best pet.

And at last she was Dad's pal as well.

Just Ask

HE: Are you Pam? And why the mask?

SHE: I can't tell, and you can't ask.

HE: I DID ask. Are you Pam?

SHE: I can't tell you if I am.

HE: Tell me why you have the mask.

SHE: My, you have a lot to ask!

(Why has Pam put on a mask?

Just so pals will have to ask!)

__mp

camp				bump
damp				dump
lamp				hump
				jump
				lump
				pump

__ft

raft	left	gift		
		lift		
		sift		

__lt

	belt			
	felt			
	melt			

48

__lf

self
elf

__lp

help
yelp

__lk

milk
silk

__ld

held

__pt

kept
wept

__ct

act

__xt

next

49

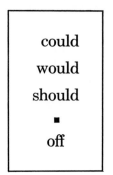

could
would
should
■
off

Jill said to Bess, "Will you get the lid off of this can?"

Bess said, "I would get it off if I could. But I can't. We should get Mom. She can get it off."

The Elf Is Back

On a bump on a log

    Was a fat, red elf.

He sat on the log

    Just to rest himself.

His cap was a sack,

    And his pants had rips.

And the elf, as he sat,

    Put his hands on his hips.

His red silk vest

Was a mess as well,

And the elf, as he sat,

Just began to yell:

"I went on a hunt,

And I set up a camp,

And the bed had lumps,

And the tent was damp.

"The bugs did jumps

On my cap and pack,

And I just felt bad,

So I left—I am back!

"I am back in Elfland—

Back!" said he.

"I am back to my pals,

As an elf should be."

Rex and the Raft

Bess had a raft and a pet dog, Rex.

She kept the raft at a dock in the big pond.

Bess and Rex went to the pond to have fun

on the raft.

"The wind is in the west," said Bess,

"and I must have help on the raft."

Rex said, "Yip!"

He ran onto the dock, and he got on the raft by himself.

Just as he got on, a gust of wind sent the raft into the pond.

Bess was left on the dock!

Bess began to yell, "Jump off, Rex! Jump off the raft!"

But Rex would not jump.

If he did, he would land in the pond.

So he just sat on the raft and let it go.

Bess could not help him.

And Rex would not help himself.

The wind kept up.

The raft hit a rock and would not go on.

"Rex is in a fix," said Bess.

"He must have help. He must have help.

If the wind would help . . ."

Just as Bess said it, the wind DID help.

A gust of wind hit the back of the raft.

Bess began to yell, "Go to the back!

Go to the back of the raft, Rex!

It will help lift the end of the raft off

the rocks!"

Rex ran to the back of the raft and sat.

The wind began to huff and puff.

At last the wind sent the raft back—

back to the dock and back to Bess.

Bess ran to get the dog.

She was not mad at Rex.

She did not yell at him.

She just sat and held him.

fl__

| | flag
flap
flat | fled | flip
flit | flop | |

sl__

| | slam
slap | sled | slid
slim
slip
slit | slop
slot | |

cl__

| | clam
clap | | clip | clod
clog | club |

pl__

	plan			plod	plug
				plop	plum
				plot	plus

gl__

| | glad | Glen | | | |

bl__

| | | bled | | blob | |
| | | | | blot | |

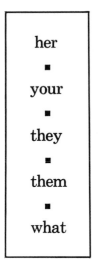

her

your

they

them

what

A hen sits on her nest.

What is in the hen's nest?

The hen has eggs in her nest.

She has six of them, and

they are big.

Bill said, "What is on your lap, Mom?"

Mom said, "Your lamp is on my lap."

"Why?" said Bill.

"It has a bad plug," Mom said.

"So I must fix it."

A Bug on a Plum

Glen had a red plum,

Red plum, red plum.

Glen had a red plum,

Yum, yum, yum!

A bug was on the red plum,

Red plum, red plum.

A bug was on the red plum,

Hum, hum, hum.

The bug bit the red plum,

Red plum, red plum.

It had a bit of red plum.

Tum, tum, tum.

Glen did a clap-slap,

Clap-slap, clap-slap.

Glen did a clap-slap,

Dum, dum, dum.

The bug did a flip-flop,

Flip-flop, flip-flop.

The bug did a flip-flop,

Pum, pum, pum.

Glen has the red plum

(No bug—just plum).

Glen has the red plum,

Yum, yum, yum!

To Be BIG

NELL: Glen! Glen! Let's have a club.

It would be fun to have a club.

Will you be in it?

GLEN: O.K., Nell. I will be in the club.

And Ann has a flag. Can she be

in the club?

NELL: Yes, yes. It would be fun to

have Ann. Let's ask her.

GLEN: Ann, Nell and I have a club.

Will you be in it?

ANN: O, yes. I will be in the club.

And I have a flag. The club must

have a flag.

NELL: O.K. We have a club and the club
has a flag. And we must get a tent.
We could put it up on the land in
back of the pond.

ANN: My dad has a tent. Let's ask him
if we can have it.

GLEN: O.K. Let's go ask him.

(Ann and Nell and Glen run to Ann's dad.)

ANN: Nell and Glen and I have a club, Dad.
We have a flag but we must have a
tent. We plan to set it up and camp
on the land in back of the pond.
Can we have your tent?

ANN'S DAD:
I have a tent, Ann, and your club can
have it. But you cannot put it up
on the land in back of the pond.

You must be BIG to camp by the pond.

ANN: O.K., Dad. Let us have the tent,

but we will not camp by the pond.

(Nell and Glen and Ann are sad.)

GLEN: Let's not be sad. I have a plan.

The club can go on a hunt.

My dad has a net. If we could

get it, we could hunt bugs on

the pond.

NELL: But, Glen, can we get your dad's net?

ANN: Let's go and ask him.

(Glen and Ann and Nell go to Glen's dad.)

GLEN: Dad! Dad! Ann and Nell and I have

a club. We could go on a hunt if

we had your net. We could hunt

bugs on the pond.

GLEN'S DAD:

> Glen, I have a net, but you cannot
> have it to hunt bugs on the pond.
> If you slip, you could end up in the
> pond. You must be BIG to hunt bugs
> on the pond.

GLEN: O.K., Dad. We are not big. We will
not hunt bugs on the pond.

(Glen and Nell and Ann are sad.)

NELL: I have it! I have it! Let's go to the
pond. We can dig clams in the mud.

ANN: But I must ask my dad if I can
dig clams.

GLEN: And I must ask my mom.

NELL: And I must ask my mom. Let's

go ask her.

(Ann and Nell and Glen run to Nell's mom.)

NELL: Mom, Glen and Ann and I have a club.

We plan to dig clams in the mud

at the pond. Can we go to the pond?

NELL'S MOM:

But Nell, the clams are in the mud.

If you slip, you will be up to your

necks in mud. No, Nell, you must be. . .

NELL, ANN, and GLEN:

. . . BIG to dig clams in the mud.

NELL: Mom, why must we be BIG to have fun?

The Plan

"What is in your hand, Tom?" said Jill.

"A flag," said Tom.

"Why?" said Ann.

"I have a plan," said Tom, and he began to flap the flag.

"Tell us your plan," said Ann.

"I will not."

"If you will not, we will ask your mom.

She will tell you to tell us," said Jill.

But Tom would not tell them.

Jill and Ann ran to Tom's mom and

said, "Tom has a plan.

But he will not tell us what it is."

But she would not help them. She said

Tom did not HAVE to tell them his plan.

Jill and Ann felt sad. Jill said,

"Why should Tom have a plan by himself?

We could help him if he would just let us."

Jill and Ann went to Bess to get help.

Jill said, "Bess, Tom has a flag.

And he said he has a plan.

But he will not tell us what the plan is.

Will you help us get Tom to tell?"

Bess said, "Yes, I will help you.

I can get Tom to tell you his plan.

Clip pins onto your hats and go to Tom.

He will ask why you have pins on your hats.

Tell him you have a club.

Tell him the pins are club pins.

He will ask you why you have a club.

But you must not tell him—not till he

tells you his plan."

"But we have no club," said Jill.

"Yes you have," said Bess. "It's a club

to get Tom to tell you his plan."

Bess put a pin on Ann's hat.

She put a pin on Jill's hat.

And Ann and Jill ran to Tom.

Tom said, "Why have you got pins on

your hats?"

Jill said, "They are club pins."

"Yes, club pins!" Ann said.

"They tell you we have a club."

"What is your club?" said Tom.

"If you tell us your plan, we will tell you what the club is," said Jill.

Tom said, "I will tell you my plan if you will tell me what your club is."

"Tell us your plan," said Jill and Ann.

Tom began to hop and jump. "My plan is a WHY plan," he said.

"A WHY plan!" said Jill and Ann. "What is a WHY plan?"

"It's a plan to get you to ask me WHY I have a flag," Tom said. "You must tell me what your club is."

Jill and Ann began to clap and yell. "It's a WHAT club," they said.

"A WHAT club!" said Tom. "What is a WHAT club?"

Jill said, "A WHAT club is a club to get you to ask us WHAT the club is! We had it just so you would tell us your plan. And you DID!"

The Pond

Flip! Flap! Flop!

Six ducks sat in a pond,

    sat in a pond.

Plip! Plap! Plop!

A raft was in the mud,

    was in the mud.

73

Slip! Slap! Slop!

The raft slid into the pond,

slid into the pond.

Clip! Clap! Clop!

The raft ran into the ducks,

ran into the ducks.

Said a duck,

"We are in luck!

Let's be glad!

Let's not be sad!

We can run!

We can jump!

We can hop!

We can bump!

We can rock!

We can slip!

We can tug!

We can flip!

O what fun

On a raft

In the sun!

sk __

		skid		
		skin		
		skip		
		skit		

st __

stab	stem		stop	stub
Stan	step			

sn __

snag		snip	snob	snub
snap				snug

sp＿

| | span
spat | sped | spin
spit | spot | spun |

sw＿

| | swam | | swim | | swum |

tw＿

| | | | twig
twin | | |

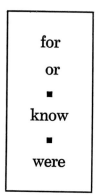

for

or

■

know

■

were

"What can we get for Miss Betts?"

"Jeff or Jill should know. They said
they would ask her what we could get for
her."

"Get a cat for her. I know she is
fond of cats."

"Were you in her cat club?"

"No. Were you?"

Six Ducks in a Pond

Six eggs were on the sand by a pond.

The eggs began to pop. Pop! Pop! Pop!

Snap! Snap! Snap!

Six bits of fuzz were on the sand.

What were the six bits of fuzz?

They were ducks!

The ducks began to get big.

And they did not just sit on the sand.

They got in back of Mom Duck and went to
the pond. "Go for a swim," said Mom Duck.

So the ducks began to step into the pond.

But not the last duck.

He would not go into the pond.

The rest of the ducks swam.

But the last duck just sat.

"I would swim if I could.

But I know I can't," he said to himself.

He was sad.

The rest of the ducks swam up to him.

They said, "Ducks swim in ponds.

You must swim if you are a duck."

The last duck said,

"What have I got to know, so I can swim?"

But the rest of the ducks could not tell

him what he had to know. They said,

"Just jump into the pond and swim."

But the last duck just sat on the sand.

"I can't swim," he said.

"I can't jump into the pond.

I will get sick if I jump in.

I can't swim if you will not help me."

"Yes you can," said the rest.

"You are a duck, and ducks MUST swim."

"Why?" he said.

"Well, the pond has bugs in it.

You can fill up on bugs if you swim.

You will not get bugs on the sand.

Step into the pond, and we will help you.

We will help you swim and get bugs."

But the last duck just sat.

He would not step into the pond.

The rest of the ducks said, "If you just sit on the sand, we can't help you." They swam off and left him by himself. They would not swim back to him.

So he got up and went to the pond.

He got his legs wet.

He went into the pond and wet his back.

He began to swim. He swam and swam.

He swam as fast as he could.

And he swam to the rest of the ducks.

The ducks were glad to have him.

"You CAN swim! You CAN swim!" they said.

"Have a bug!"

Stan's Test

Stan went into his mom's den.

He was sad, and he said,

"My pals and I were up on the hill.

They had sleds, but I did not.

Will you get me a sled, Mom?"

His mom said, "You should have a sled.

And you CAN have a sled if you pass a test!

I will get you a big sled."

"But you know I can sled on a hill, Mom.

Why must I pass a test?" said Stan.

"My test is not a sled test," said Mom.

"It is a test to GET a sled."

"O.K., Mom," said Stan.

"Let me have the test. I can pass it."

(You should help Stan if you can.)

Stan's mom said, "Tell me, Stan:

Can a step step? Can a tent tent?

Can a duck duck? Can a rock rock?

Can a mop mop? Can a box box?

Can a pin pin? Can a peg peg?"

"I can pass the test, Mom," Stan said.

"I know a step can't step and a tent can't

tent. But a duck can duck.

And a rock can rock. And a mop can mop.

But a box can't box. A pin can pin.

But a peg can't peg. Did I pass?"

Stan's mom said, "You know a lot.

But tell me, Stan:

Can you step on a step?

Can you rock on a rock?

Can you pump a pump?

Can you land on land?

Can you flap a flap?"

Stan said, "I can pass the test, Mom.

I know I can step on a step.

I can rock on a rock.

I can pump a pump.

I can land on land.

And I can flap a flap.

Did I pass the test, Mom?"

"Yes, Stan, you did pass," Mom said.

"So I will get you a big sled."

(Did you help Stan pass his test?)

The Top

Flip! Flop!

Flip! Flop!

Spins the top!

Spins the top!

It tips and rocks.

It spins and bends.

It cannot stop

Till its spin ends.

Flip! Flop!

Flip! Flop!

Spins the top!

Spins the top!

br___

Brad brag brat		brim		

gr___

grab	Greg	grin grip		

dr___

drab drag		drip	drop	drug drum

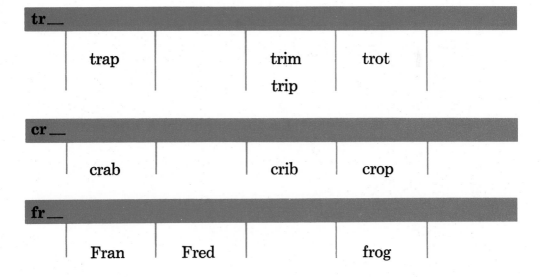

tr__

| | trap | | | trim
trip | trot | |

cr__

| | crab | | | crib | crop | |

fr__

| | Fran | Fred | | | frog | |

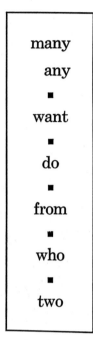

many

any

▪

want

▪

do

▪

from

▪

who

▪

two

"Mom, I <u>want</u> to put up a tent, but I <u>do</u> not have <u>any</u> pegs," Jill said.

"If you <u>want</u> to put up a tent," her mom said, "you must have <u>many</u> pegs."

"<u>Do</u> you know <u>who</u> has <u>any</u>?" said Jill.

"I have <u>two</u>," said her mom. "And Glen will let you have <u>two</u>. And you can get <u>two</u> <u>from</u> Stan."

"Six is not <u>many</u>," said Jill.

"Six will <u>do</u>," said her mom.

The Best Band

We want the best band in the land.

Who can we get to be in the band?

Who can bump a drum?

Who can slam a bell?

Who can clap and hum?

Who can jump and yell?

Well, Brad can bump a drum,

And he can clap and hum.

And Fran can slam a bell

And jump and yell as well.

So Brad and his pal Fran will do.

They could BE a band—just the two!

Act 1

FRAN: Skip, let's go to the pond and swim.

It's hot, and a swim would . . .

SKIP: O.K., Fran. But I must ask my

mom or dad. I do not swim well, and

they said I must ask them if I want

to go to the pond.

(Fran and Skip go to Skip's dad.)

SKIP: Dad, can I go for a swim in the

pond?

Fran will go, and she swims well.

She can grab me if I slip.

DAD: If Fran will go, you can go.

But Mom and I plan to go on a

trip, so you must be back at six.

SKIP: O.K., Dad. I will not forget.

I will be back by six.

(Fran and Skip go to the pond.)

FRAN: I am glad your dad said yes.

It's fun to swim in the pond.

And we can trap a crab or two,

Or we can hunt for frogs.

SKIP: Yes, Fran, it's fun to swim.

But I want to trap a crab.

FRAN: We must go to the rocks to trap

crabs. Let's go.

I have a can, and you can have it.

We will put a bit of ham in the

can and set it by a rock.

A crab will slip into it to get

the ham.

SKIP: The can is a trap?

FRAN: Yes. The crab will grab the ham.

And you can snap a lid on the can.

You will have a crab for your mom.

But do not let the crab grab you.

You know what a crab can do.

SKIP: I know. Let me have the can.

I will get a crab for Dad and Mom.

(Skip puts a bit of ham into the can and

sets it by a rock.)

SKIP: Fran! Fran! I got it!

A crab went into the trap.

But I forgot what to do next.

FRAN: Put a lid on the can, Skip!

Snap on the lid, or the crab will

grab you!

(As Skip puts the lid on the trap, his leg

hits a rock and he slips.

He spins and sits—ON THE CRAB!

The crab snaps at Skip and gets a grip on

his pants.)

SKIP *(He yells):*

Fran! Dad! Mom! Help! My back!

A crab is on my back! Get it off!

Get it off, Fran! I am not ham!

(Fran runs up, but cannot help.

Skip runs from the pond.

He runs as fast as the wind.

He runs to his dad.)

SKIP: Dad! Mom! Help!

I sat on a crab, and it bit me.

In fact, the crab is on my back.

Get it off, Dad! Get the crab off!

DAD: O.K., Skip. I will get it off.

Just bend on my lap.

I will slap the crab.

(Skip and the crab get a slap from Dad.

The crab drops to the rug.)

DAD: If you are at the pond, you should

not slip and sit on a crab, Skip.

But I am glad you did.

SKIP: Glad! Why?

DAD: The crab let you know you should

get back. It is ten past six.

And you were to be back at six.

You forgot.

So the crab was a big help!

Gram's Plan

Fran went to Gram and said, "Gram, will you get a sled for me?"

Fred went to Gram and said, "If you get a sled for Fran, will you get me a sled?"

The twins ran to Gram, and THEY said, "Gram, we want two sleds! Get us two sleds!"

Gram said, "I can't get so many sleds. I would if I could, but I can't. I want you to have fun, but I can't get so many sleds."

Fran and Fred and the twins were sad.

And Gram? Well, she was not glad.

"What can we do, Gram?" Fran said.

"We want to sled on the hill.

It's lots of fun."

Gram said, "I have a plan," and she left.

She was back at sunset. "You can be glad,"

she said.

"Why can we be glad?" Fran said.

"We are sad. We have no sleds."

"Yes," said Fred, "we are sad.

You said we can't have any sleds."

"I said you can't have MANY sleds,"

Gram said. "Let's go to the top of the hill.

I have a gift for you."

Fred, Fran, and the twins ran up the hill.

Gram ran up the hill—huff-puff!

A big bobsled was at the top of the hill.

"What a big sled!" said Fran.

"Is it my sled?"

"Is it my sled?" said Fred.

"Is the sled for us?" said the twins.

"The big sled is for Fran, Fred, AND the twins," said Gram.

But Fran, Fred, and the twins were not glad. They said, "A big sled is not fun. It will not go fast if so many are on it."

"Yes, it will!" said Gram.

"It's a bobsled. Get on. It will go fast."

Gram held the bobsled as Fran, Fred, and the twins got on.

The bobsled began to slip.

It began to go fast.

It went as fast as it could.

It slid fast past a log.

It slid fast past a flag.

It slid fast past a bump.

104

"Help! Help!" The twins began to yell as the big sled went on and on. "The bobsled can't stop!"

But at last the big bobsled did stop.

It hit a bump!

Flip! Flop! Fran, Fred, and the twins fell off the sled.

But they got up and began to grin.

They went up the hill to Gram.

They ran as fast as they could.

As they ran, they began to yell, "It's fun, Gram! It's fun!

A bobsled IS fun. We have a sled!"

Brad and the Frog

Brad sat to rest next to a pond.

A big rock was in the pond.

And a fat frog was on the rock.

Brad said to himself, "A frog can hop.

It can skip and swim. But if I can trap

it, I can have it for a pet."

So Brad set a trap by the rock in the pond.

The frog began to hop and jump.

It went off the rock and into the pond.

It swam up to the trap.

It swam past it and back to the rock.

It swam up and back, up and back.

"The frog knows I set a trap for it,"
Brad said. "And it wants to have fun.

It wants to get me mad.

But I will get it yet!"

The frog swam up to the mud and sat in it.

Brad said, "I will jump into the mud and
grab you, frog!"

But Brad fell into the pond and got
wet up to his neck. He was mad.

"I will grab you yet, frog!" he began

to yell. "You WILL be my pet!"

But the frog just sat in the mud.

Brad swam to the mud as fast as he could.

The frog did a hop, skip, and jump.

Plop! It was on a log.

Brad had to step on a rock to get at

the frog. But the rock was wet.

Brad began to slip! *Plop!*

Brad was back in the pond.

But Brad did NOT yell.

And Brad was NOT mad. He just said,

"You do not want to be my pet, do you?

Well, you win, frog.

I will just have to let you go."

And as a wet Brad left the pond, he said

to himself, "Did the frog grin at me?"

The Best Fox in the Land

A fox met Mrs. Frog at the well.

Mrs. Frog had a sack of plums on her back.

The fox said to himself, "A sack of

plums is just what I want.

And I know what I can do to get them."

"Mrs. Frog," said the fox,

"what a big sack of plums you have!

Just two of them are as big as you, and

you have a sack of them!

Who are the plums for?"

"Mrs. Crab is sick," said Mrs. Frog.

"The plums are for her.

They will help her get well."

The fox began to grin.

He said to Mrs. Frog, "Let me help you get
the plums to Mrs. Crab. You should rest.
Put the plums on my back."

Mrs. Frog said, "O, Mr. Fox, I am so
glad to have your help.
You are the best fox in the land."

So Mrs. Frog put the sack of plums on the fox's back.

The two of them set off for Mrs. Crab's.

They went ten steps, and the fox said, "Mrs. Frog, you cannot go as fast as I can. I will go on to Mrs. Crab so she can have her plums. I will drop back and get you." And the fox began to trot.

Mrs. Frog began to hop fast. She said, "Mr. Fox, if you go to Mrs. Crab's by yourself, you will not drop back to get me. In fact, you will not GO to Mrs. Crab's."

"I know," said the fox. And he began to run. "But you can tell Mrs. Crab what big plums she would have had—if you had not met the best fox in the land."

The fox sped off.

Mrs. Frog had to act fast.

She had just a skip and a jump left in her.

SKIP—and she was just in back of the fox.

JUMP—and she was on the fox's back.

Mrs. Frog was so fast, the fox did not

know she was on his back.

The fox ran on as fast as he could.

He ran and ran. He ran on and on.

At last he began to drag his legs.

He could not lift them.

So he had to stop and rest.

But just as he did, Mrs. Frog slid from
his back. And she had the bag.

She said, "O, Mr. Fox, it was a fast trip!

You do not know it, but we are just two

steps from Mrs. Crab's.

She will have her sack of plums.

And I will tell her I met THE BEST FOX

IN THE LAND!"

__ll

		smell	drill	
		spell	grill	
		swell	skill	
			spill	
			still	

__ss

brass	bless	bliss		
class	dress			
glass	press			
grass				

__ff

staff		cliff		bluff
		sniff		gruff
		stiff		stuff

__ck

black	speck	brick	block	pluck
crack		click	clock	stuck
smack		flick	flock	truck
snack		slick	stock	
stack		stick		
track		trick		

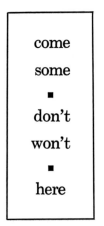

come

some

■

don't

won't

■

here

Mom said to Greg, "Won't you come here and help me dig some clams?"

Greg said, "I don't want to come yet."

"Why don't you want to come?" Mom said.

"What if some crabs got into my trap?" said Greg.

"Well, go to the trap," said Mom. "But come here as fast as you can. If you don't, you won't get any clams. I will have to dig them up myself."

The Trick Clock

The twins, Jack and Jill, got a gift.

The gift was in a big box.

They were so glad to get a gift, they began

to hop and skip.

"I can tell," Jack said, "it's a truck

for me and a drum for you."

"I can tell," Jill said, "it's a tent

for me and blocks for you."

They began to lift up the box's lid.

"Tick-tock! Tick-tock!" went the gift.

The twins sat still—as still as rocks.

"It's not a truck or a drum," said Jill.

"It's not a tent or blocks," said Jack.

"It's just a CLOCK!" said Jill.

And it was. A big clock was in the box.

"A clock won't be any fun," said Jack.

"I don't want a clock," said Jill.

"What can a clock do?" said Jack.

"Let's just put it in the den."

They left the big clock in the den.

As they left the den, the clock said:

"Tick-tock! Tick-tock!

Don't the twins know

I am a trick clock?

I am a trick clock!

Tick-tock! Tick-tock!"

Its ticks were sad. Its tocks were sad.

But the twins did not stop.

They did not know what the clock had said.

They did not know it was a trick clock.

"I don't want to be sad," said the clock.

"And I do want the twins to be my pals.
I have a plan."

At six, the twins went back to the den.
As they went past the clock, it said,

"Tick-tock! Tick-tock!

I am a trick clock!

I am a trick clock!

Tock-tick! Tock-tick!

What a trick! What a trick!"

Jack said, "Come here, Jill.

Tell me if a clock can go 'tock-tick'?"

"No," said Jill, "it cannot.

A clock must go 'tick-tock, tick-tock.'

It cannot go 'tock-tick.' "

But the big glass clock said,

"Tick-tock! Tick-tock!

I am a trick clock!

I am a trick clock!

And here is my trick:

I can go TOCK-TICK!"

The twins began to hop and skip.

"It's a trick clock!" said Jill.

"Yes, it's a trick clock!" said Jack.

And the clock said,

"Tick-tock! Tick-tock!

I am a trick clock!

I am the twins' clock!

Tock-tick! Tock-tick!

What a trick! What a trick!"

So the twins were glad to have the gift.

It was not JUST a clock.

It was a trick clock!

Jim's Dog, Sniff

Sniff was Jim's pet dog.

She had black spots on her back and legs.

Jim and Sniff had lots of fun.

But Jim's pals would ask him,

"What fun is your pet? What fun is Sniff?

She won't jump or run to get a stick.

She won't hunt. She won't do tricks.

So what fun is she?"

Sniff would not hunt or do any tricks.

If Jim got set to go on a hunt, Sniff

ran from him and hid.

And she hid till Jim got back from the hunt.

Jim said to his pals,

"Sniff can smell tracks for blocks."

But his pals said, "So what?

She runs from you if you want her to hunt."

As Jim sat by himself, his mom ran up.

"Jim, come and help," she said.

"Flip, the cat, went up the big hill.

He is on a cliff, and he won't come back.

I went up to the cliff to hunt for him.

But I could not get to him.

I must have your help."

"I don't know if I can help," said Jim.

"But Sniff can."

"She can?" said Jim's mom.

"Yes," said Jim, "she can help.

She can smell Flip's tracks. She can get him."

Jim ran and got Sniff.

"Come on, Sniff," said Jim.

"Here is Flip's bed. Get to know his smell."

So they went to Flip's bed.

Sniff had a sniff at it.

"We must get to the cliff fast," said

Jim. "We must get Flip for Mom."

So Jim and Sniff ran up to the cliff.

Sniff ran on top of the rocks.

She began to sniff the rocks for Flip.

Sniff ran into the grass.

She got to some cat tracks.

At last she got to Flip.

He was in a crack next to a big rock.

His leg was stuck in the crack.

Sniff began to yelp for Jim.

Jim ran up to help.

He ran to Flip and began to pet him.

He began to tug at Flip's leg.

"I can lift you up!" he said to Flip.
And he did.

"Your leg just has a bump on it."

Jim held Flip, and they went back to Mom.

Mom was glad to get Flip.

She held the cat in her lap to pat it.

And Sniff got a snack.

Jim went to get his pals.

He just had to tell them what Sniff did.

"Sniff can hunt!" he said to them.

"Flip was in a bad spot, but

Sniff went and got him!"

The Grill

The hotdog grill

    At the end of the block

Has lots of smells

    And a big glass clock.

Cliff Black is the man

    Who runs the grill.

He grins at me

    As I know he will.

He spills some stuff

On a hotdog bun

And sticks in a dog.

Next comes the fun!

My hand grabs the bun,

And my lips go *smack!*

In six big gulps

I have had my snack.

Camp Six-by-Six

Lizz Glass was ten, so she could go to

camp. But the twins could not go.

The twins, Fran and Sam, were just six.

And Mrs. Black, who ran the camp, had said,

"The twins must be ten to come to camp."

Lizz had fun at camp.

She swam in the camp's pond.

She went on trips on the camp's rafts.

She would hunt for frogs and crabs.

Fran and Sam were sad. They said,

"It's hot here, but we can't go to camp.

Lizz has fun, but we can't."

"I will ask Mom what to do," said Sam.

So he went to his mom and said,

"Camp is a lot of fun for Lizz.

But Fran and I can't go. So we are sad.

We have a pond, but it's not big.

So we can't swim in it. What can we do?"

Mom said, "You should have fun.

You should swim if you want to.

And I will tell you what we can do."

Fran and Sam began to jump. "Tell us!

Tell us what to do," they said.

Mom said, "I will get some bricks.

You get some sand. You will have fun."

"O.K., Mom," said Fran and Sam.

Fran and Sam got some sand.

And Mom got a lot of bricks.

They put the bricks in stacks by the pond.

They put bags of sand on top of the bricks.

"I know what it is," said Fran.

"It's a dam!"

"Yes, it is," said Mom.

"And do you know what it will do?"

"I do!" said Sam.

"The dam will let the pond get big!"

And it did. The pond began to get big.

Fran and Sam began to yell,

"The pond will get big and we can swim!"

Mom said, "A raft can't fit in it.

And it won't have any frogs or crabs.

But you CAN swim in it.

And your pals on the block can come.

You and your pals can swim in the pond."

Fran said, "We have a camp at last.

It will be CAMP SIX-BY-SIX—for Sam and

I are six."

The Elf Gets Help

Nick and Nell began to go up a hill.

They were still many steps from the top.

But Nick said, "I can't go on.

My legs are stiff. Let's stop and rest."

Just as they sat, Nell began to yell,

"Nick, the hill has a big crack in it!"

"What an odd crack!" said Nick.

"I want to go back."

"O no, don't go back," Nell said.

Just as she said it, the crack began to

snap and click.

And the grass bent, but not from the wind.

Nick and Nell kept as still as they could.

And an elf slid from the crack in the hill!

The elf said, "I am an elf. I am an elf. And I just can't help myself!"

Nick and Nell sat as still as rocks.

The elf was as odd as an elf can be.

He had a black cap, vest, and pants.

And his neck was fat.

"Who—wh—what do you want?" said Nick.

"I must have help," said the elf.

"Will you help me?"

"We can help if we know what you want,"
said Nell.

"And I would tell you what I want,"
the elf said. "But I forgot!
You will help if you can tell me what it was."

Nick said, "WE can't tell you.
WE can't tell you, if you forgot it yourself.
You should go back to Elfland.
In Elfland they will know what you forgot."

"No, no!" said the elf. "I can't.
I can't go back to Elfland.
An elf should not forget."

The elf sat on a log and wept.

"Don't be so sad," said Nell.

"We will do the best we can to help."

"Will you?" said the elf.

He began to clap his hands.

"Did you forget your pack?" said Nick.

"Did you forget your mom or your dad?"
said Nell.

"No, no!" said the elf.

"Don't be sad," said Nell.

"I will let you have some milk and a bun."

She got up from the grass.

She sat by the elf. But he just wept.

"I will let you have some plums,"

said Nick. He put a plum in the elf's hand.

The elf bit into it.

He began to jump. He began to yell.

"My neck! My neck!"

"What is it?" said Nick.

"I know what it is," the elf said.

"I know what I forgot!"

"What is it?" said Nick and Nell.

They could not sit still.

The elf put his hands on his neck and

began to do a jig.

"I forgot I have the mumps!" he said.

The elf went back to the crack.

"I am so glad you could help me," he said.

"I am so glad you had a plum.

I won't forget you!"

And he slid back into the crack.

"We will get the mumps!" said Nick.

But the elf did not know what he said, for he was back in Elfland.

Nick was sad as he sat on the grass. "What can we do?" he said. "The elf had mumps. We will get mumps."

Nell sat next to him and began to grin.

"Don't be sad," she said.

"You can't get the mumps from an elf. And we did help him!"

"Yes," said Nick. "And I am glad."

They got up from the grass and went on to the top of the hill.

Pattern page (section 1, pages 2-3)

_ll					
		bell	Bill	doll	dull
		fell	fill		gull
		Nell	hill		hull
		sell	Jill		
		tell	kill		
		well	mill		
		yell	pill		
			till		
			will		

_ss					
	lass	Bess	hiss		fuss
	mass	less	kiss		muss
	pass	mess	miss		Russ

__ff

		Jeff			cuff
					huff
					puff

__zz

			fizz		buzz
					fuzz

__dd

	add			odd	

__nn

	Ann		inn		

__gg

		egg			

Pattern page (section 2, pages 15-16)

_ck				
back	deck	Dick	cock	duck
Jack	neck	kick	dock	luck
pack	peck	lick	lock	suck
sack		Nick	rock	tuck
tack		pick	sock	
		Rick		
		sick		
		tick		

be
he
me
we
she

Pattern page (section 3, pages 25-26)

_nd

band	bend	wind	fond	
hand	lend		pond	
land	mend			
sand	send			
and	end			

_nt

can't	bent	hint		hunt
pants	dent	mint		
ant	lent	tint		
	rent			
	sent			
	tent			
	went			

Mr.

Mrs.

■

put

147

Pattern page (section 4, pages 36-37)

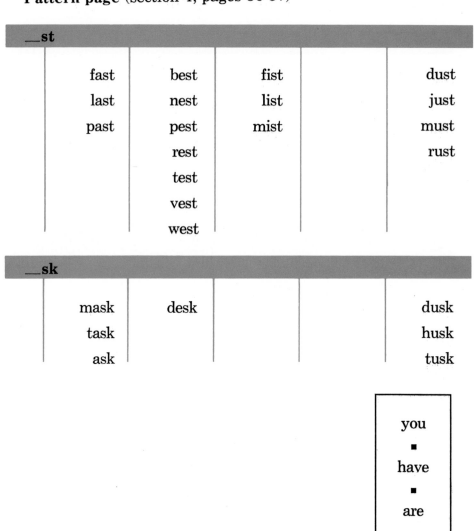

__st				
fast	best	fist		dust
last	nest	list		just
past	pest	mist		must
	rest			rust
	test			
	vest			
	west			

__sk				
mask	desk			dusk
task				husk
ask				tusk

you

■

have

■

are

Pattern page (section 5, pages 48-50)

__mp				
camp				bump
damp				dump
lamp				hump
				jump
				lump
				pump

__ft				
raft	left	gift		
		lift		
		sift		

__lt				
	belt			
	felt			
	melt			

__lf				
	self			
	elf			

__lp

help
yelp

__lk

milk
silk

__ld

held

__pt

kept
wept

__ct

act

__xt

next

could
would
should
■
off

Pattern page (section 6, pages 58-60)

fl__

	flag flap flat	fled	flip flit	flop

sl__

	slam slap	sled	slid slim slip slit	slop slot

her
■
your
■
they
■
them
■
what

cl__

	clam clap		clip	clod clog	club

pl__

	plan			plod plop plot	plug plum plus

gl__

	glad	Glen		

bl__

		bled		blob blot

151

Pattern page (section 7, pages 76-78)

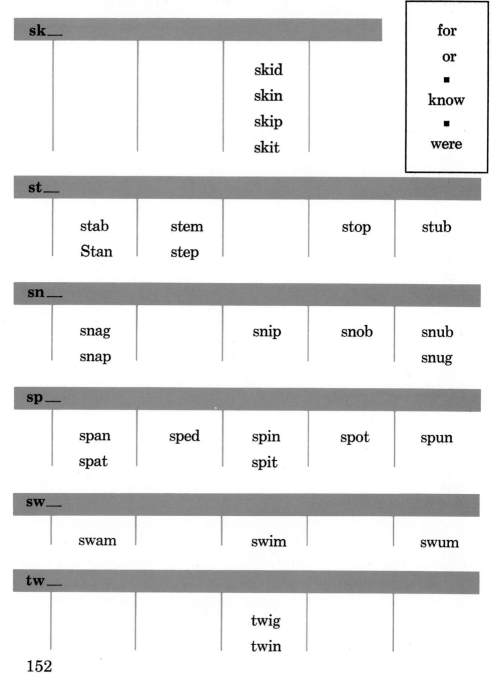

sk__

		skid	
		skin	
		skip	
		skit	

for
or
■
know
■
were

st__

| stab | stem | | stop | stub |
| Stan | step | | | |

sn__

| snag | | snip | snob | snub |
| snap | | | | snug |

sp__

| span | sped | spin | spot | spun |
| spat | | spit | | |

sw__

| swam | | swim | | swum |

tw__

| | | twig | |
| | | twin | |

Pattern page (section 8, pages 90-92)

br__

Brad brag brat		brim	

gr__

grab	Greg	grin grip	

dr__

drab drag		drip	drop	drug drum

tr__

trap		trim trip	trot

cr__

crab		crib	crop

fr__

Fran	Fred		frog

many

any

■

want

■

do

■

from

■

who

■

two

153

Pattern page (section 9, pages 116-118)

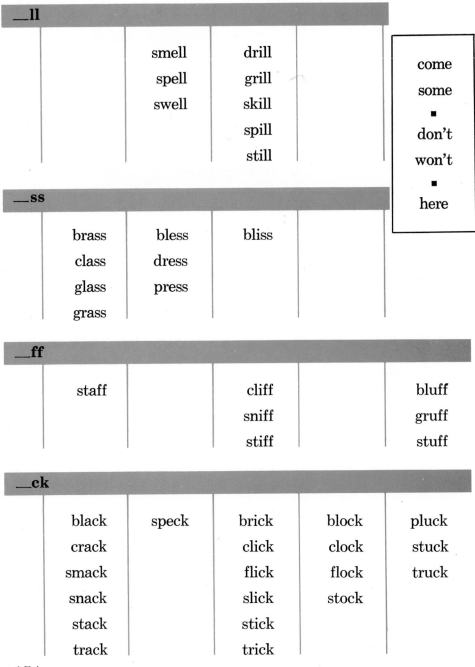

__ll				
		smell	drill	
		spell	grill	
		swell	skill	
			spill	
			still	

__ss				
	brass	bless	bliss	
	class	dress		
	glass	press		
	grass			

__ff				
	staff		cliff	bluff
			sniff	gruff
			stiff	stuff

__ck				
	black	speck	brick	block	pluck
	crack		click	clock	stuck
	smack		flick	flock	truck
	snack		slick	stock	
	stack		stick		
	track		trick		

come

some

■

don't

won't

■

here

154